Simple Solutions.

Minutes a Day-Mastery for a Lifetime!

Level 2

Mathematics

2nd Edition

2nd Semester

Nancy L. McGraw

Bright Ideas Press, LLC
Cleveland, OH

Simple Solutions Level 2 Second Edition

2nd semester

Printed in the United States of America

ISBN-13: 978-1-934210-32-1
ISBN-10: 1-934210-32-3

Cover Design: Dan Mazzola
Editor: Kimberly A. Dambrogio

Welcome to

Simple

Solutions

Note to the Student:

This workbook will give you the opportunity to practice skills you have learned in previous grades. By practicing these skills each day, you will gain confidence in your math ability.

Using this workbook will help you understand math concepts more easily and for many of you, will give you a more positive attitude towards math in general.

In order for this program to help you be successful, it is extremely important that you do a lesson every day. It is also important that you check your answers and ask your teacher for help with the problems you didn't understand or that you did incorrectly.

If you put forth the effort, Simple Solutions will change your opinion about math forever.

Lesson #73

1. Write the name of the shape.

2. $856 - 294 = ?$

3. How many months are in a year?

4. Write the standard number for *five hundred seventy-two*.

5. 964 ◯ 694

6. Which is longer, five inches or five feet?

7. $538 + 379 = ?$

8. What fraction out of five is shaded?

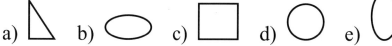

9. $\$16.79 + \$23.55 = ?$

10. Which of the shapes are ellipses?

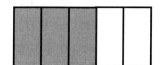

a) ◺ b) ⬭ c) ▢ d) ◯ e) ⬯ f) ▭

11. Which digit is in the tens place in the number *741*?

12. Write a fact family for 6, 9 and 15.

13. $4 + 7 = ?$

14. What is the value of the coins?

15. Ellen has 85¢ . If she buys a bag of chips for 35¢ and a pack of gum for 30¢, how much money will she have left?

1.	2.	3.
4.	5.	6.
7.	8.	9.
10.	11.	12.
13.	14.	15.

Lesson #74

1. $23 + 44 + 31 = ?$

2. Draw two <u>congruent</u> rectangles.

3. Which number comes next?　45,　55,　65, _____

4. Round *46* to the nearest ten.

5. What time is it?

6. $952 - 339 = ?$

7. Write the name of each shape.　a)　　b)

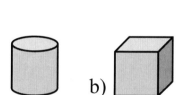

8. $17 - 8 = ?$

9. Write the month that comes before March.

10. Order these numbers from greatest to least.　832,　245,　916,　740

11. If you have six quarters, how much money do you have?

12. 318 ◯ 183

13. There were 37 boats in the dock and another 15 out on the lake. How many boats were there in all?

14. Draw a square and shade $\frac{1}{4}$ of it.

15. Who collected the smallest number of cans?

    How many more cans did Becky collect than Lee?

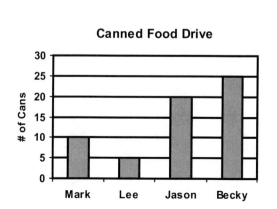

1.	2.	3.
4.	5.	6.
7.	8.	9.
10.	11.	12.
13.	14.	15.

Lesson #75

1. $56 + 44 = ?$

2.   What is the length of the pen, in inches?

3.   Fill in the missing numbers.   80, 90, ____, 110, ____

4.   Is the number *523* even or odd?

5.   Round *32* to the nearest ten.

6.   Write the time.

7. $950 - 428 = ?$

8.   How much money is shown here?

9.   Is a good night's sleep about 8 hours or 8 minutes?

10.   Two figures with the same size and shape are _____.

11.   What are the first four even numbers?

12. $\$33.25 + \$14.77 = ?$

13.   Which digit is in the ones place in *653*?

14. $8 + 7 + 5 = ?$

15.   A toad jumped 6 inches on its 1st jump, 7 inches on its 2nd jump, and 4 inches on its last jump. How many inches did the toad jump altogether?

1.	2.	3.
4.	5.	6.
7.	8.	9.
10.	11.	12.
13.	14.	15.

Lesson #76

1.   144 + 668 = ?

2.   **A <u>line of symmetry</u> divides a shape into two equal parts.** Draw a triangle and show a line of symmetry.

3.   Write *forty-eight* as a standard number.

4.   What part of the circle is shaded?

5.   How much money is ten nickels?

6.   877 – 325 = ?

7.   Write the name of the shape that has three sides.

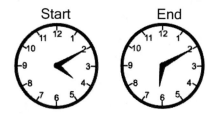

8.   How much time has passed?

9.   Which tally marks show *12*?

a) 卌   b) 卌 卌 || c) 卌 ||

10. Is *318* an even number or an odd number?

11. What number comes between *79* and *81*?   79 ____ 81

12. 703 ◯ 713

13. Draw 2 congruent circles.

14. On which day of the week is May 12th?

15. What will be the date, two weeks after May 2nd?

| May | | | | | | |
S	M	T	W	T	F	S
					1	2
3	4	5	6	7	8	9
10	11	12	13	14	15	16
17	18	19	20	21	22	23
24	25	26	27	28	29	30
31						

1.	2.	3.
4.	5.	6.
7.	8.	9.
10.	11.	12.
13.	14.	15.

Lesson #77

1. $14.27 + $13.35 = ?

2.   What is the name of the shape?

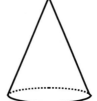

3.   531 – 155 = ?

4.   Does a pencil weigh more than a pound or less than a pound?

5.   8 + 8 = ?

6.   What is the time?

7.   Write *315* using words.

8.   If you have 5 dimes and 4 pennies, how much money do you have?

9.   What number comes just before *400*?

10.   Draw a square. Show a line of symmetry.

11.   503 ◯ 56

12.   Round *55* to the nearest ten.

13.   Count by twos.   68, ____, 72, _____, 76, _____

14.   How much money is shown?

15.   Joel had 30 pieces of candy. If he gives 23 pieces to his friends, how many pieces of candy will Joel have left?

1.	2.	3.
4.	5.	6.
7.	8.	9.
10.	11.	12.
13.	14.	15.

Lesson #78

1. The answer to what type of problem is called the sum?

2. $32 + 15 + 10 = ?$

3. There were one hundred thirty-three birds in the tree. Sixty-seven of them flew away. How many birds are still in the tree?

4. Which digit is in the hundreds place in *249*?

5. Eight quarters are how much money?

6. Write the time shown on the clock.

7. $730 - 319 = ?$

8. Which is longer, 7 inches or 7 feet?

9. Round *87* to the nearest ten.

10. Draw a triangle. Show a line of symmetry.

11. What fraction of the rectangle is shaded?

12. $316 + 316 = ?$

13. How many inches are in a foot?

14. Which month is 2 months after April?

15. In all, how many books did the children read?

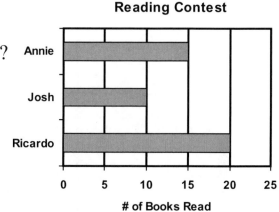

Reading Contest

1.

2.

3.

4.

5.

6.

7.

8.

9.

10.

11.

12.

13.

14.

15.

Lesson #79

1. **The <u>mode</u> is the number that is seen most often in a set.** In the set of numbers (13, 26, 15, 13), the mode is 13. The number 13 is seen more than any other number. Write *mode* in the box.

2. $117 + 568 = ?$

3. What time is it?

4. 516 ◯ 332

5. Which is more money, 12 dimes or 5 quarters?

6. Write the missing numbers.   130, 140, ____, 160, ____, 180

7. $88 - 59 = ?$

8. Round *16* to the nearest ten.

9. Draw two congruent ovals.

10. $5 + 6 = ?$

11. Which shape is divided exactly in half? Draw it in the box.

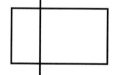

12. Write *242* using words.

13. Does a watermelon weigh more than or less than a pound?

14. What is the name of this shape?

15. Ryan had $2.50. He spent $1.15 on candy. How much money does he have left?

1.	2.	3.
4.	5.	6.
7.	8.	9.
10.	11.	12.
13.	14.	15.

Lesson #80

1.   36 + 59 = ?

2.   What is the mode of this set of numbers?   9, 16, 8, 14, 8

3.   What is the answer to a subtraction problem called?

4.   53 ◯ 56

5.   What month is 2 months before December?

6.   Round *19* to the nearest ten.

7.   950 – 236 = ?

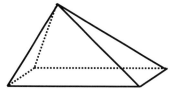

8.   Name the shape.

9.   How many days are in a year?

10. Is the number *851* even or odd?

11. Write the time.

12. What fraction of the rectangle is shaded?

13. Fill in the missing numbers.   300, ____, 500, 600, ____

14. Congruent figures have the _____ size
     and the _____ shape.

15. What is the date 3 weeks after August 5th?

     September 1st will be on which day of the
     week?

August

S	M	T	W	T	F	S
		1	2	3	4	5
6	7	8	9	10	11	12
13	14	15	16	17	18	19
20	21	22	23	24	25	26
27	28	29	30	31		

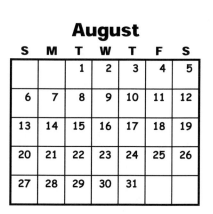

1.	2.	3.
4.	5.	6.
7.	8.	9.
10.	11.	12.
13.	14.	15.

Lesson #81

1. 219 ◯ 192

2. Round *52* to the nearest ten.

3. Two figures with the same size and shape are _____.

4. $9 + 9 + 9 = ?$

5. What is the mode of this set of numbers?   26, 14, 33, 14, 40

6. $\$36.12 - \$18.38 = ?$

7. How much time has passed?

8. What is the length of the paintbrush, in inches?

9. What number follows *999*?

10. How many days are in three weeks?

11. What fraction of the box is shaded?

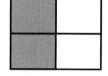

12. $735 + 167 = ?$

13. Which is greater, 8 quarters or $1.00?

14. I have four tens and six ones. What number am I?

15. At the zoo, the fourth graders saw 16 sharks and 8 whales. How many sharks and whales did they see altogether?

1.	2.	3.
4.	5.	6.
7.	8.	9.
10.	11.	12.
13.	14.	15.

Lesson #82

1. What is the time shown on the clock?

2. Count by twos. 38, ___, 42, ____, 46

3. How many inches are in 2 feet?

4. $520 - 255 = ?$

5. Round *93* to the nearest ten.

6. How much money is 2 quarters and 3 dimes?

7. $27 + 52 + 19 = ?$

8. Draw a rectangle and shade 3 out of 5 parts.

9. Which digit is in the ones place in *378*?

10. What is the name of the shape that is shown?

11. Does a bicycle weigh more than a pound or less than a pound?

12. Draw two congruent ellipses.

13. There are _____ minutes in one hour.

14. Draw a square. Show a line of symmetry on the square.

15. **Use the chart below to answer the questions.**

    Which holiday was the least favorite?

    How many more students chose Halloween than chose Valentine's Day?

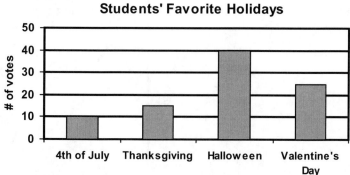

1.	2.	3.
4.	5.	6.
7.	8.	9.
10.	11.	12.
13.	14.	15.

Lesson #83

1.   59 – 36 = ?

2.   Round *88* to the nearest ten.

3.   The sum is the answer to a(n) _____ problem.

4.   Write the time shown on the clock.

5.   5 + 9 = ?

6.   Write *639* using words.

7.   98 ◯ 135

8.   Jeremy rode 24 miles on Friday. He rode 18 miles on Saturday and 32 miles on Sunday. How many miles did he ride in all?

9.   What number comes just before *1,000*?

10.   How much money is pictured here?

11.   743 + 187 = ?

12.   Write the first five odd numbers.

13.   The number that occurs most often in a set of numbers is the _____.

14.   3 + 3 + 3 = ?

15.   What fraction of the rectangle is shaded?

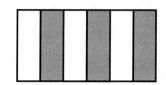

1.	2.	3.
4.	5.	6.
7.	8.	9.
10.	11.	12.
13.	14.	15.

Lesson #84

1. Round *74* to the nearest ten.

2. 86 ◯ 74

3. Which digit is in the ones place in *563*?

4. Is the number *85* even or odd?

5. $319 + 499 = ?$

6. Does a button weigh more than or less than a pound?

7. Write the missing numbers in the list. 130, 140, ___, 160, ___, 180

8. $64 - 28 = ?$

9. Which is greater, 3 quarters or 10 dimes?

10. What is the name of this shape?

11. How many minutes are in a half-hour?

12. How much time has passed?

13. An amusement park had 535 visitors on Friday and 675 visitors on Saturday. How many visitors did they have in all?

14. What fraction of the shape is shaded?

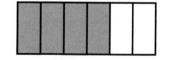

15. Which shape shows a line of symmetry? Draw it in the box.

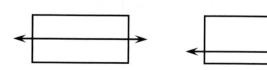

1.	2.	3.
4.	5.	6.
7.	8.	9.
10.	11.	12.
13.	14.	15.

Lesson #85

1.   806 ◯ 806

2.   What fraction of the square is shaded?

3.   Round *22* to the nearest ten.

4.   **The answer to a multiplication problem is the <u>product</u>.** Write the word *product* in the box.

5. $\$55.35 + \$27.55 = ?$

6.   Write *724* using words.

7.   What is the name of this shape?

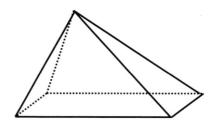

8. $98 + 64 = ?$

9.   What time is it?

10. Draw 2 congruent triangles.

11. $536 - 254 = ?$

12. How much money is shown?

13. What is the mode of 26, 34, 15, 26 and 42?

14. $2 + 2 + 2 = 6$ **Three groups of 2 is six. Another way to write this is $3 \times 2 = 6$.** Write *3 × 2 = 6* in the box.

15. What is the date of the first Saturday in June?

     On what day of the week is June 15th?

June

S	M	T	W	T	F	S
				1	2	3
4	5	6	7	8	9	10
11	12	13	14	15	16	17
18	19	20	21	22	23	24
25	26	27	28	29	30	

1.	2.	3.
4.	5.	6.
7.	8.	9.
10.	11.	12.
13.	14.	15.

Lesson #86

1.   Write a fact family for 5, 7 and 12.

2. $36 + 12 + 24 = ?$

3. $842 \bigcirc 1,000$

4.   Write the time shown on the clock.

5.   Round *13* to the nearest ten.

6.   Which is greater, 10 nickels or 4 dimes?

7.   Draw a square and show a line of symmetry.

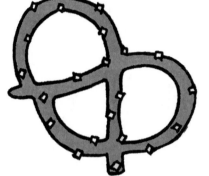

8.   Count by fives.   35, 40, ___, ___, ___

9. $635 - 272 = ?$

10. I have 7 hundreds, 4 tens and 3 ones. What number am I?

11. Harry is 5 years older than Susan. Susan is 2 years younger than Nick. Nick is 10 years old. How old is Harry?

12. Is *460* an even number or an odd number?

13. The answer to a subtraction problem is the _____.

14. Does a pretzel weigh more than or less than a pound?

15. Write a multiplication sentence for $2 + 2 + 2 + 2$.

1.	2.	3.
4.	5.	6.
7.	8.	9.
10.	11.	12.
13.	14.	15.

Lesson #87

1. Round *47* to the nearest ten.

2. $5 + 5 + 5 + 5 = ?$

3. The answer to an addition problem is called the _____ .

4. $\$87.25 - \$32.75 = ?$

5. What is the name of the shape?

6. Find the mode of 22, 41, 13, 41 and 62.

7. How much is shaded? Write the fraction.
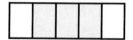

8. $336 + 256 = ?$

9. What time is shown on the clock?

10. Sam bought a box of candy that costs $1.25. He gave the clerk $2.00. How much change should Sam get back?

11. What number comes between *599* and *601*?

12. How many days are in three weeks?

13. Which digit is in the ones place in *864*?

14. $0 \times 2 = ?$

15. How many boats were on the lake?

    How many more motor boats than canoes were on the lake?

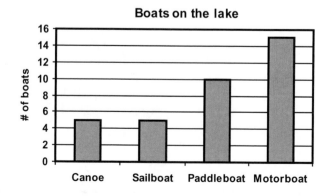

1.	2.	3.
4.	5.	6.
7.	8.	9.
10.	11.	12.
13.	14.	15.

Lesson #88

1. Which shape shows a line of symmetry? Draw it in the box.

2. $9 + 8 = ?$

3. Round *69* to the nearest ten.

4. What is the value of the coins?

5. $2 \times 2 = ?$

6. How many inches are in a foot?

7. $89 - 64 = ?$

8. How much time has passed?

9. $427 + 386 = ?$

10. $5 + 5 + 5 = ?$

11. Which month is two months before September?

12. What part is <u>not</u> shaded? Write a fraction.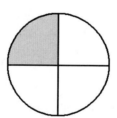

13. Find the mode of this set of numbers.   10, 15, 17, 15, 19

14. Two figures with the same size and shape are _____ .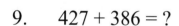

15. Amanda spent $1.25 on candy and $1.40 on a drink. How much money did she spend altogether?

1.	2.	3.
4.	5.	6.
7.	8.	9.
10.	11.	12.
13.	14.	15.

Lesson #89

1.　$628 - 372 = ?$

2.　What is the mode of 56, 39, 70, 21 and 39?

3.　$1 \times 2 = ?$

4.　Round *76* to the nearest ten.

5.　508 ◯ 518

6.　Draw two congruent ellipses.

7.　How many months are in one year?

8.　$38 + 16 + 21 = ?$

9.　What time is shown on the clock?

10.　I have six tens and five ones. What number am I?

11.　The answer to a multiplication problem is the _____.

12.　Which is more money, 6 dimes or 2 quarters?

13.　What fraction is shaded?

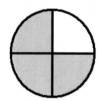

14.　Write $2 + 2 + 2 + 2$ as a multiplication sentence and solve it.

15.　There are 30 students in one second grade class and 26 students in the other. How many second graders are there in all?

1.	2.	3.
4.	5.	6.
7.	8.	9.
10.	11.	12.
13.	14.	15.

Lesson #90

1.　Carol had eight jars. She put two marbles in each jar. How many marbles were there altogether? (Draw a picture to help you.)

2.　$129 + 456 = ?$

3.　Round *43* to the nearest ten.

4.　Write the time shown on the clock.

5.　$2 \times 5 = ?$

6.　The number *257* has _____ hundreds, _____ tens and _____ ones.

7.　Give the name of each shape.

  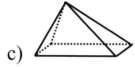

　a)　　　　　　b)　　　　　c)

8.　$75 - 58 = ?$

9.　What fraction is shaded?

10.　$5 + 5 + 5 + 5 = ?$

11.　How much money is shown?

12.　Write the first six even numbers.

13.　Two figures with the same size and shape are _____.

14.　What number comes just before *1,000*?

15.　The number that is seen most often in a set of numbers is the

　　　a) sum.　　　b) mode.　　　c) product.

1.	2.	3.
4.	5.	6.
7.	8.	9.
10.	11.	12.
13.	14.	15.

Lesson #91

1. Draw a circle and show a line of symmetry.

2. $6 \times 2 = ?$

3. What will be the time 30 minutes after 2:00?

4. Round *83* to the nearest ten.

5. The answer to a(n) _____ problem is the product.

6. $556 + 258 = ?$

7. Is the number *376* even or odd?

8. $5 + 5 + 5 = ?$

9. Write a fact family for 6, 7 and 13.

10. $93 - 48 = ?$

11. Which is longer, 7 inches or 7 feet?

12. Find the mode of 28, 13, 31, 13 and 74.

13. Draw two different 4-sided shapes and name them.

14. If Allen saves 10¢ each day for 9 days, how much money will he have at the end of 9 days?

15. What will be the date 3 weeks after October 5th?

    November 1st will be on which day of the week?

October

S	M	T	W	T	F	S
	1	2	3	4	5	6
7	8	9	10	11	12	13
14	15	16	17	18	19	20
21	22	23	24	25	26	27
28	29	30	31			

1.	2.	3.
4.	5.	6.
7.	8.	9.
10.	11.	12.
13.	14.	15.

Lesson #92

1. Write the standard number for *seven hundred fifty-two*.

2. 364 ◯ 463

3. Round *77* to the nearest ten.

4. $198 + 364 = ?$

5. Write the missing numbers from the list.   250, ____, 270, 280, ____

6. Which is more money, $2.00 or 7 quarters?

7. What time is shown on the clock?

8. $2 + 2 + 2 + 2 + 2 = ?$

9. Draw a triangle with a line of symmetry.

10. Annie has 95¢. If she buys a pack of laces for her rollerblades that cost 56¢, how much money does she have left?

11. $24 - 8 = ?$

12. **A round, solid shape is called a sphere.** **A basketball is a sphere.** Write *sphere* in the box.

13. The answer to a(n) _____ problem is the difference.

14. $7 \times 2 = ?$

15. Which fraction is greater?

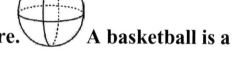

$\dfrac{1}{3}$ ◯ $\dfrac{1}{2}$

1.	2.	3.
4.	5.	6.
7.	8.	9.
10.	11.	12.
13.	14.	15.

Lesson #93

1. Draw 2 congruent hearts.

2. $72 - 49 = ?$

3. Write the odd numbers between *20* and *26*.

4. $1 \times 5 = ?$

5. What is the time 30 minutes after 3:00?

6. Which shaded part is greater?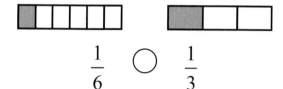

    $\dfrac{1}{6}$ $\bigcirc$ $\dfrac{1}{3}$

7. $26 + 9 + 31 = ?$

8. Seven groups of two is how many?

9. The sum is the answer to a(n) _____ problem.

10. 89 $\bigcirc$ 96

11. What is the mode of 27, 16, 32, 18 and 27?

12. $516 + 279 = ?$

13. Is a swing set about 6 feet tall or 6 inches tall?

14. How many days are in one year?

15. How many more cans than bottles were collected?

    How many items were collected altogether?

Recycling	
Item	# Collected
Bottles	12
Cans	34
Papers	55

1.	2.	3.
4.	5.	6.
7.	8.	9.
10.	11.	12.
13.	14.	15.

Lesson #94

1. Round *18* to the nearest ten.

2. $73 + 28 = ?$

3. Which is greater, 5 nickels or 3 dimes?

4. What is the name of the shape?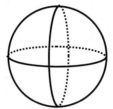

5. $172 - 89 = ?$

6. Draw 2 congruent triangles.

7. Find the mode of 13, 28, 13, 17, 28 and 13.

8. What fraction is shaded?

9. The product is the answer to a(n) _____ problem.

10. Which even numbers come between *31* and *35*?

11. $8 \times 2 = ?$

12. Which digit is in the tens place in *806*?

13. $5 \times 10 = ?$

14. Draw a rectangle and show a line of symmetry.

15. In an aquarium there are 16 goldfish, 10 angelfish and 4 clownfish. How many fish are in the aquarium?

1.	2.	3.
4.	5.	6.
7.	8.	9.
10.	11.	12.
13.	14.	15.

Lesson #95

1. 50¢ – 15¢ = ?

2. Write the name of the shape.

3. How many inches are in a foot?

4. Is this a line of symmetry?

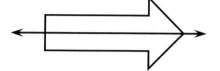

5. 107 + 496 = ?

6. There were 38 poodles in the dog show. If twelve poodles drop out of the show, how many poodles are left?

7. What part of the square is shaded?

8. Round *67* to the nearest ten.

9. How much time has passed?

Start   End

10. 5 × 2 = ?

11. What is the shape of a tennis ball?

   a) cube   b) cone   c) sphere

12. What temperature is shown on the thermometer?

13. Which shaded fraction is greater?

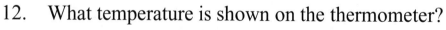

$$\frac{1}{4} \bigcirc \frac{1}{3}$$

14. 3 × 2 = ?

15. Two figures with the same size and the same shape are _____.

1.	2.	3.
4.	5.	6.
7.	8.	9.
10.	11.	12.
13.	14.	15.

Lesson #96

1. $5 + 5 + 5 + 5$ is the same as 4×5. Both are equal to _____.

2. What is the mode of this set of numbers?   36, 19, 41, 25, 19

3. Round *93* to the nearest ten.

4. What time is shown on the clock?

5. $508 + 196 = ?$

6. Write *67* using words.

7. What is the value of the coins?

8. Draw 2 congruent squares.

9. Is a basketball hoop about 9 feet tall or 9 inches tall?

10. Count by twos.   98, ____, ____, 104, ____

11. $4 + 9$ is the same as _____ $+ 5$. Both are equal to 13.

12. List the odd numbers between *40* and *44*.

13. What is the shape of a can?   a) pyramid b) cone c) cylinder

14. Which shaded part is greater?

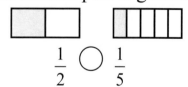

$$\frac{1}{2} \bigcirc \frac{1}{5}$$

15. June 1st will be on which day of the week? What is the date one week after May 11th?

May						
S	**M**	**T**	**W**	**T**	**F**	**S**
				1	2	3
4	5	6	7	8	9	10
11	12	13	14	15	16	17
18	19	20	21	22	23	24
25	26	27	28	29	30	31

1.	2.	3.
4.	5.	6.
7.	8.	9.
10.	11.	12.
13.	14.	15.

Lesson #97

1. There are eight counters that will be put into groups. If there are 2 counters in each group, how many groups are there?

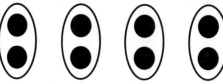

2. The answer to a multiplication problem is the _____.

3. 70¢ – 18¢ = ?

4. What time is shown on the clock?

5. 10 + 10 + 10 is the same as 3 × 10. Both are equal to _____.

6. Is a coffee pot about 1 inch or 1 foot tall?

7. **There are 4 quarts in a gallon.** Write *4 quarts = 1 gallon.*

8. 333 + 475 = ?

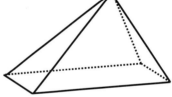

9. What is the name of this shape?

10. Which digit is in the ones place in *813*?

11. Is this a line of symmetry?

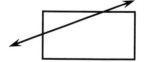

12. 602 ◯ 612

13. How many days are in a year?

14. Which is greater, 2 quarters or 6 dimes?

15. Mia has $1.50. Does she have enough money to buy a pen for 60¢ and a notebook for 95¢?

1.	2.	3.
4.	5.	6.
7.	8.	9.
10.	11.	12.
13.	14.	15.

Lesson #98

1. There were 24 cupcakes on the table at the beginning of the party. By the end of the party there were only 9 cupcakes left on the table. How many cupcakes were eaten during the party?

2. $1 \times 10 = ?$

3. $316 + 525 = ?$

4. What will be the time 30 minutes after 8:00?

5. $2 + 2 + 2 + 2 + 2 + 2$ is the same as 6×2. Both are equal to _____.

6. A jack-in-the-box has what solid shape?

    a) cube   b) cone   c) sphere

7. How many quarts are in a gallon?

8. Are these shapes congruent?

9. $60 - 24 = ?$

10. How much is shaded? Write the fraction.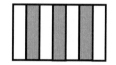

11. Find the mode of this list of numbers.   60, 42, 39, 51, 42

12. There are ten counters on a table. If they are grouped with 5 counters in each group, how many groups are there?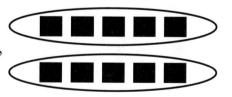

13. $5 + 9 = ?$

14. How much money do you have if you have 6 quarters?

15. Draw a heart and show a line of symmetry.

1.	2.	3.
4.	5.	6.
7.	8.	9.
10.	11.	12.
13.	14.	15.

Lesson #99

1.   How many quarts are in a gallon?

2. $88 + 38 = ?$

3.   What fraction of the counters is shaded?

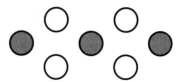

4.   Round *39* to the nearest ten.

5.   How much time has passed?

6. $0 \times 5 = ?$

7.   Draw 2 congruent circles.

8. $2 \times 2 = ?$

9.   How much money is shown?

10. $654 - 82 = ?$

11.   What number comes right after *605*?

12.   Write the even numbers between *21* and *25*.

13.   There were 5 rafts on the river. In each raft there were 3 children. How many children were there in all?

14.   Choose the number that comes between *157* and *171*.

     a) 132   b) 150   c) 164

15.   What are the two most popular lunch foods?

    How many students like tacos and burgers best?

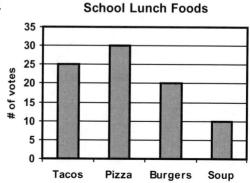

1.

2.

3.

4.

5.

6.

7.

8.

9.

10.

11.

12.

13.

14.

15.

Lesson #100

1. How much money is shown?

2. $354 - 98 = ?$

3. $4 \times 2 = ?$

4. There are _____ quarts in a gallon.

5. Is this a line of symmetry?

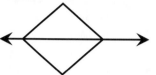

6. $5 + 5 + 5 + 5 + 5$ is the same as 5×5. Both are equal to _____.

7. What fraction of this rectangle is shaded?

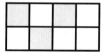

8. $36 + 8 + 22 = ?$

9. What time is it?

10. $964 \bigcirc 1{,}000$

11. **When you share equally, you divide. The sign "÷" means divide.** 12 counters altogether, with 2 in each group is equal to how many groups? $12 \div 2 = ?$

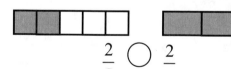

12. Which fraction is greater?

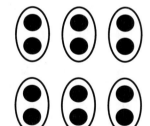

13. $15 - 6 = ?$

$\dfrac{2}{5} \bigcirc \dfrac{2}{3}$

14. Write the standard number for *two hundred sixteen*.

15. How many inches long is the line segment?

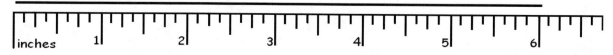

1.	2.	3.
4.	5.	6.
7.	8.	9.
10.	11.	12.
13.	14.	15.

Lesson #101

1.   450 − 36 = ?

2.   Write the name of the shape in the box.

3.   Round *66* to the nearest ten.

4.   9 + 2 + 7 = ?

5.   How much money is shown?

6.   Draw 2 congruent rectangles.

7.   0 × 5 = ?

8.   The answer to an addition problem is the _____.

9.   Fill in the missing numbers.   230, ____, 250, ____, ____

10.   What fraction of this box is shaded?

11.   3 × 2 = ?

12.   615 + 327 = ?

13.   325 ◯ 340

14.   10 ÷ 5 = ?

15.   How many inches long
      is the rectangle?

1.

2.

3.

4.

5.

6.

7.

8.

9.

10.

11.

12.

13.

14.

15.

Lesson #102

1. Two figures with the same size and shape are _____.

2. Is this a line of symmetry?

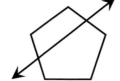

3. Round *29* to the nearest ten.

4. $7 \times 2 = ?$

5. What is the mode of this set of numbers?   21, 14, 16, 12, 14

6. $5 + 6$ is the same as _____ $+ 8$. Both are equal to 11.

7. How many quarts are in a gallon?

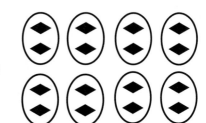

8. $16 \div 2 = ?$ (Hint: How many groups of 2?)

9. $553 + 219 = ?$

10. What time is it?

11. $90¢ - 35¢ = ?$

12. How many months are in two years?

13. Are these shapes congruent?

14. Would a drinking straw weigh more than or less than a pound?

15. Chan has 68¢. His mother gives him 3 dimes and then he buys a pencil for 18¢. How much money does he have now?

1.	2.	3.
4.	5.	6.
7.	8.	9.
10.	11.	12.
13.	14.	15.

Lesson #103

1. Write the number *209* using words.

2. $53 + 9 = ?$

3. What fraction of the rectangle is shaded?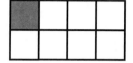

4. $9 \times 2 = ?$

5. There are 15 muffins on a plate. Eight of them are banana muffins. How many are not banana muffins?

6. $0 \times 2 = ?$

7. $650 - 249 = ?$

8. Write the time shown on the clock.

9. Which is greater, 2 dollars or 9 quarters?

10. Is the number *937* even or odd?

11. $6 + 4 = ?$

12. Which digit is in the tens place in *521*?

13. Use tally marks to show the number *16*.

14. $66 \bigcirc 121$

15. Write the length of the line segment in inches.

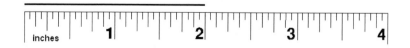

1.	2.	3.
4.	5.	6.
7.	8.	9.
10.	11.	12.
13.	14.	15.

Lesson #104

1. Are these shapes congruent?

2. Round *72* to the nearest ten.

3. How much money is shown?

4. $640 - 322 = ?$

5. Which fraction is greater?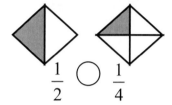

6. $10 \times 2 = ?$

$\frac{1}{2}$ $\frac{1}{4}$

7. Four children plant tulips. If each child plants 5 tulips, how many tulips do they plant in all? Make a picture to help you.

8. How many inches are in a foot?

9. Write the name of this shape.

10. $3 + 3 + 3 + 3 + 3$ is the same as 5×3. Both are equal to _____.

11. There are _____ quarts in a gallon.

12. $14 \div 2 = ?$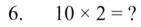

13. In the number *851* which digit is in the hundreds place?

14. Write *93* using words.

15. How many days are in the month of January?

    On which day of the week is January 25th?

January

S	M	T	W	T	F	S
				1	2	3
4	5	6	7	8	9	10
11	12	13	14	15	16	17
18	19	20	21	22	23	24
25	26	27	28	29	30	31

1.	2.	3.
4.	5.	6.
7.	8.	9.
10.	11.	12.
13.	14.	15.

Lesson #105

1.　$96 - 54 = ?$

2.　What is the name of this shape?　

3.　How many days are in one year?

4.　$304 \bigcirc 329$

5.　Keisha saves magazines. She has five stacks and each stack has 10 magazines in it. How many magazines has Keisha saved?

6.　$43 + 8 + 26 = ?$

7.　Does this circle have a line of symmetry?　

8.　Which is more money, 9 dimes or 10 nickels?

9.　How much time has passed?　

10.　$2 \times 5 = ?$

11.　Is an envelope about 9 inches long or 9 feet long?

12.　Draw a rectangle. Shade 3 parts out of 5 parts.

13.　$10 + 10 + 10$ is the same as 3×10. Both are equal to _____.

14.　Does a gallon of milk weigh more than or less than a pound?

15.　Find the length of the crayon in inches.

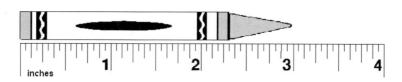

1.	2.	3.
4.	5.	6.
7.	8.	9.
10.	11.	12.
13.	14.	15.

Lesson #106

1. $44 - 16 = ?$

2. Draw a square and show a line of symmetry on it.

3. The answer to a multiplication problem is the _____.

4. $6 \times 10 = ?$

5. Juan planted 2 rows of pine trees with 6 trees in each row. How many trees did Juan plant?

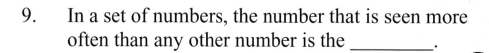

6. Round *15* to the nearest ten.

7. $713 + 68 = ?$

8. List the even numbers between *51* and *55*.

9. In a set of numbers, the number that is seen more often than any other number is the _____.

10. $0 \times 5 = ?$

11. If you have 7 dimes and 2 nickels, how much money do you have?

12. In the number *510* which digit is in the tens place?

13. $24 + 13 + 8 = ?$

14. Write the missing numbers in the sequence.   15, 20, ___, 30, ____

15. Is this figure a cone?

1.	2.	3.
4.	5.	6.
7.	8.	9.
10.	11.	12.
13.	14.	15.

Lesson #107

1.   How many quarts are in a gallon?

2. $7 + 9 = ?$

3.   What time is it?

4. $16 \div 2 = ?$ (Hint: 16 counters in all with 2 in each group. How many groups?)

5. $480 \bigcirc 590$

6.   How much money is shown?

7. $121 + 98 = ?$

8.   Finish the pattern. 200, 300, _____, 500, 600, ___, 800, ___, 1,000

9. $1 \times 5 = ?$

10. Are these figures congruent?

11. $60¢ - 31¢ = ?$

12. Write the number that has 3 hundreds, 5 tens, and 2 ones in it.

13. The difference is the answer to a(n) _____ problem.

14. Write the standard number for *six hundred twenty-nine*.

15. How many bags of leaves were collected on Tuesday and Thursday?

     On which day were the most bags collected?

Leaf Collection	
Day	Bags Collected
Monday	🌷🌷
Tuesday	🌷🌷🌷🌷
Wednesday	🌷🌷🌷
Thursday	🌷🌷
Friday	🌷

Each 🌷 stands for 2 bags

1.	2.	3.
4.	5.	6.
7.	8.	9.
10.	11.	12.
13.	14.	15.

Lesson #108

1.   How many months are in a year?

2.   What is the value of the coins?

3. $88 + 29 = ?$

4. $2 \times 5 = ?$

5.   Which shape shows $\frac{1}{4}$?   a)    b)   c)

6.   Tori has 3 bags of goldfish. If each bag has 5 fish in it, how many fish does Tori have? Draw a picture to help you.

7.   Round *11* to the nearest ten.

8.   What is the name of this shape?

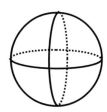

9. $730 - 85 = ?$

10.   What time is shown on the clock?

11. $6 \times 10 = ?$

12.   Draw 2 congruent ellipses.

13.   The symbol "×" tells you to _____.

        a) add   b) subtract   c) multiply

14.   Does a leaf weigh more than or less than a pound?

15.   How many quarts are in 2 gallons?

1.	2.	3.
4.	5.	6.
7.	8.	9.
10.	11.	12.
13.	14.	15.

Lesson #109

1. $346 + 285 = ?$

2. Draw 2 rectangles that are not congruent.

3. Round *55* to the nearest ten.

Start   End

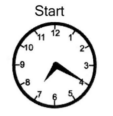 

4. How much time has passed?

5. $8 \times 2 = ?$

6. How many quarts are in a gallon?

7. What fraction of the rectangle is shaded?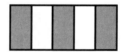

8. The answer to a multiplication problem is the _____.

9. $470 - 138 = ?$

10. Which heart is divided into 2 equal parts? Draw it.

11. $893 \bigcirc 887$

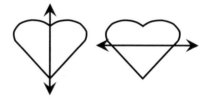

12. $1 \times 10 = ?$

13. Find the mode of this set of numbers.   14, 22, 35, 14, 45

14. Which is greater, 2 quarters or 6 dimes?

15. Write the length of the pencil in inches.

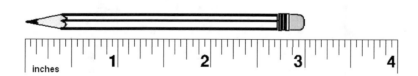

1.	2.	3.
4.	5.	6.
7.	8.	9.
10.	11.	12.
13.	14.	15.

Lesson #110

1. $12 \div 2 = ?$ (Hint: 12 objects altogether can be broken into how many groups, if there are 2 objects in each group?)

2. $36¢ + 19¢ = ?$

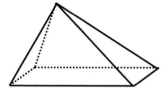

3. What is the name of this figure?

4. Fill in the missing numbers. 45, ____, 65, ____, 85

5. How much money is shown?

6. $45 + 26 + 8 = ?$

7. $573 - 96 = ?$

8. $10 + 10 + 10 + 10$ is the same as 4×10. Both are equal to _____.

9. What time is it?

10. $5 \times 5 = ?$

11. What do you call the number that is seen most often in a set of numbers?

12. Does a slice of bread weigh more than or less than a pound?

13. Write the standard number for *six hundred forty-seven*.

14. A butterfly has 4 wings. How many wings are on 5 butterflies? Draw a picture to help you.

15. Patti ate $\frac{1}{6}$ of the pie. Ty ate 3 pieces of the pie. Who ate more pie?

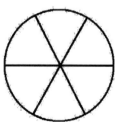

1.	2.	3.
4.	5.	6.
7.	8.	9.
10.	11.	12.
13.	14.	15.

Lesson #111

1. $388 + 96 = ?$

2. Are these shapes congruent?

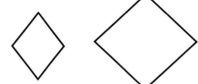

3. How much money is 10 quarters?

4. Round *94* to the nearest ten.

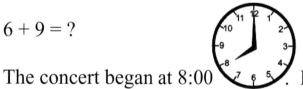

5. Which fraction is greater? $\frac{1}{3} \bigcirc \frac{1}{2}$

6. The sum is the answer to a(n) _____ problem.

7. Write the odd numbers between *30* and *36*.

8. How many quarts are in a gallon?

9. Which would you use to measure the temperature outside?

      a) ruler   b) thermometer   c) scale

10. $6 + 9 = ?$

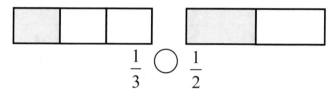

11. The concert began at 8:00 . It ended at 9:30 . How long did the concert last?

12. Does this show a line of symmetry?

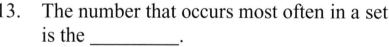

13. The number that occurs most often in a set is the _____.

14. I have 6 hundreds, 3 tens and 2 ones. What number am I?

15. How many days are in November?

On which day of the week is Nov. 14th? Nov. 1st?

		November				
S	M	T	W	T	F	S
1	2	3	4	5	6	7
8	9	10	11	12	13	14
15	16	17	18	19	20	21
22	23	24	25	26	27	28
29	30					

1.	2.	3.
4.	5.	6.
7.	8.	9.
10.	11.	12.
13.	14.	15.

Lesson #112

1.   Which number follows *99*?

2.   2 + 2 + 2 + 2 is the same as 4 × 2. Both are equal to _____.

3.   It is 6:00 now. What time will it be in 20 minutes?

4.   518 + 264 = ?

5.   Write the symbol that tells you to multiply.

6.   Use tally marks to show the number *13*.

7.   8 ÷ 2 = ? (Hint: How many groups of 2?)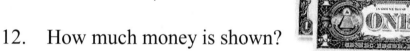

8.   Does a ladybug weigh more than a pound or less than a pound?

9.   434 ◯ 443

10. What fraction of the figure is shaded?

11. 750 – 329 = ?

12. How much money is shown?

13. Which digit is in the ones place in *623*?

14. Ellen bought a pen for $2.50 and a tablet for $1.35. How much money did Ellen spend on these supplies?

15. How long is the arrow?

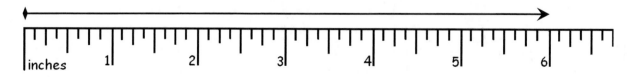

1.	2.	3.
4.	5.	6.
7.	8.	9.
10.	11.	12.
13.	14.	15.

Lesson #113

1. What time is shown on the clock?

2. $97 + 35 = ?$

3. $5 + 5 + 5 + 5$ is the same as 4×5. Both are equal to _____.

4. Find the mode of 27, 50, 13, 41 and 27.

5. Is *948* an even number or an odd number?

6. The play began at 8:30 p.m. and ended at 10:00 p.m. How long was the play?

7. $14 \div 2 = ?$ (Hint: how many groups of 2?)

8. There are _____ quarts in a gallon.

9. $0 \times 2 = ?$

10. How much money is shown?

11. $724 - 361 = ?$

12. The product is the answer to a(n) _____ problem.

13. Write *176* using words.

14. In the number *807*, which digit is in the tens place?

15. What temperature is shown on the thermometer?

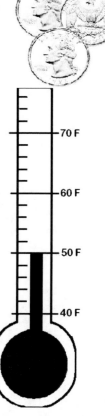

1.	2.	3.
4.	5.	6.
7.	8.	9.
10.	11.	12.
13.	14.	15.

Lesson #114

1. $1 \times 5 = ?$

2. Is the line on the figure a line of symmetry?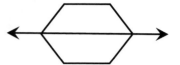

3. $556 + 374 = ?$

4. Write the symbol that tells you to subtract.

5. Ricardo planted 3 rows of tomato plants. Each row had 5 plants in it. How many tomato plants did Ricardo plant?

6. Count by twos.   56, ____, ____, 62, ____

7. Round *71* to the nearest ten.

8. Draw 2 squares that are not congruent.

9. Does a bag of groceries weigh more than or less than a pound?

10. Write the name of each shape.

    a)   b)   c)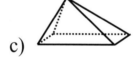

11. How much time has passed?

12. $5 + 5 + 5$ is the same as 3×5. Both are equal to ____.

13. $84 - 29 = ?$

14. How many inches are in a foot?

15. How long, in inches, is the piece of gum?

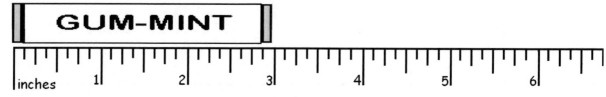

1.	2.	3.
4.	5.	6.
7.	8.	9.
10.	11.	12.
13.	14.	15.

Lesson #115

1. Which shaded part shows $\frac{1}{4}$? Draw it in the box.

    a)  b) c)

2. 316 ◯ 163

3. There were 18 jelly beans left in the jar. Julie put the 18 jelly beans into groups of 2. How many groups of 2 did Julie make?

4. $618 + 176 = ?$

5. Which digit is in the thousands place in *3,419*?

6. Draw a triangle and show a line of symmetry on it.

7. How much money do you have if you have 8 nickels?

8. Does a dictionary weigh more than a pound or less than a pound?

9. A party hat has the same shape as which solid?

10. Write the time shown on the clock.

11. $259 - 64 = ?$

12. Round *27* to the nearest ten.

13. Which number comes between *135* and *230*?   415   121   205

14. $0 \times 2 = ?$

15. Whose swim lesson is the longest?
     What time is the 6 – 9 year-old lesson?

Swim Lessons	
Age (yrs.)	Time
3 - 5	9:00 − 9:30
6 - 9	9:30 − 10:00
10	10:00 − 11:00

1.	2.	3.
4.	5.	6.
7.	8.	9.
10.	11.	12.
13.	14.	15.

Lesson #116

1. Which is longer, 3 weeks or 1 month?

2. $14 + 12 + 22 = ?$

3. What is the name of the shape?

4. $2,356 \bigcirc 1,295$

5. Two figures with the same size and the same shape are _____.

6. $2 \times 2 = ?$

7. Find the mode of this set of numbers.   10, 13, 18, 10, 19

8. Write the time shown on the clock.

9. $751 - 239 = ?$

10. Which digit is in the hundreds place in *5,207*?

11. What fraction of the rectangle is shaded?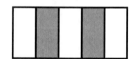

12. How many quarts are in a gallon?

13. How much money is shown?

14. $5 + 5 + 5$ is the same as 3×5. Both are equal to _____.

15. Mrs. Thomas' house has three floors. There are 5 rooms on the first floor, 4 rooms on the second floor and 5 rooms on the third floor. How many rooms are in Mrs. Thomas' house?

1.	2.	3.
4.	5.	6.
7.	8.	9.
10.	11.	12.
13.	14.	15.

Lesson #117

1. $89¢ - 37¢ = ?$

2. There were one hundred twenty-five people at the zoo on Friday. There were two hundred sixty-six people at the zoo on Saturday. How many people were at the zoo on Friday and Saturday?

3. Draw two congruent hearts.

4. Is the number *385* even or odd?

5. $564 + 277 = ?$

6. $5 \times 5 = ?$

7. Does this picture show a line of symmetry?

8. Which digit is in the thousands place in *5,831*?

9. What fraction is not shaded?

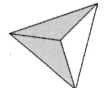

10. $2,527 \bigcirc 2,257$

11. Is a couch about 6 inches long or 6 feet long?

12. Fill in the missing numbers.   230, 240, ____, 260, ____

13. Round *46* to the nearest ten.

14. How many inches are in a foot?

15. July 1st will be on which day of the week?

    The play is 2 weeks from June 6th. What is the date of the play?

| June | | | | | | |
S	M	T	W	T	F	S
		1	2	3	4	5
6	7	8	9	10	11	12
13	14	15	16	17	18	19
20	21	22	23	24	25	26
27	28	29	30			

1.

2.

3.

4.

5.

6.

7.

8.

9.

10.

11.

12.

13.

14.

15.

Lesson #118

1.   Write the even numbers between *61* and *65*.

2. $353 - 137 = ?$

3.   How much money is shown?

4.   How many quarts are in a gallon?

5. $2 + 2 + 2 + 2 + 2 + 2$ is the same as 6×2. Both are equal to ____.

6.   Write the time shown on the clock.

7. $43 + 99 = ?$

8.   How many days are in 2 years?

9.   What is the name of this shape?

10. $1 \times 10 = ?$

11.   The answer to a subtraction problem is the _____.

12.   What is the length of the bat, in inches?

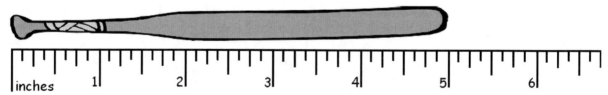

13.   Which number comes just before *1,000*?

14.   Write *597* using words.

15.   There were 385 people at the water park on Thursday. On Friday, 675 people visited the water park. How many more people were at the water park on Friday than on Thursday?

1.	2.	3.
4.	5.	6.
7.	8.	9.
10.	11.	12.
13.	14.	15.

Lesson #119

1. $8 \times 2 = ?$

2.   What fraction of this shape is shaded?

3.   There were 6 boats on the lake on Saturday. Each boat had 5 people aboard. How many people were in all six boats? Use a drawing to help you.

4.   How many months are in 2 years?

5.   Write the name of the shape.

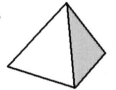

6.   How much time has passed?

7. $533 + 457 = ?$

Start   End

8.   List the odd numbers between *80* and *86*.

9. $6 \div 2 = ?$

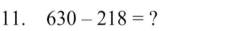

10.   The product is the answer to a(n) _____ problem.

11. $630 - 218 = ?$

12.   Which shaded part is greater?

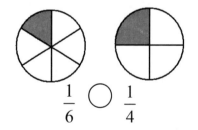

$\frac{1}{6}$ $\bigcirc$ $\frac{1}{4}$

13.   How much money is 7 quarters?

14.   Round *68* to the nearest ten.

15.   Which class is the longest? How long is it?

     What time does math class start?

Class Schedule	
8:30 − 9:00	Spelling
9:00 − 10:00	Reading
10:00 − 10:30	Math

1.	2.	3.
4.	5.	6.
7.	8.	9.
10.	11.	12.
13.	14.	15.

Lesson #120

1.   What is the mode in this set of numbers?   22, 16, 35, 10, 35

2.   Write the time shown on the clock.

3. $10 \times 5 = ?$

4.   983 ◯ 1,000

5.   What number follows *1,255*?

6.   How many inches are in a foot?

7.   Which digit is in the tens place in *4,075*?

8.   Write the temperature shown on the thermometer.

9.   How much money is ten dimes?

10.   Round *265* to the nearest hundred.

11.   Is the number *7,323* even or odd?

12.   There are _____ quarts in a gallon.

13.   Is a telephone about 8 inches long or 8 feet long?

14. $2 + 2 + 2$ is the same as 3×2. Both are equal to _____.

15.   There were 6 sunflowers in the garden. Each sunflower had 10 petals. How many petals were there altogether? Draw a picture to help you.

1.	2.	3.
4.	5.	6.
7.	8.	9.
10.	11.	12.
13.	14.	15.

Lesson #121

1. Which is longer, 8 months or 1 year?

2. $36 + 25 + 12 = ?$

3. Draw 2 congruent circles.

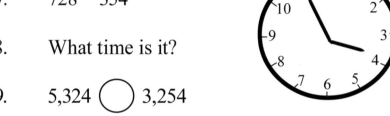

4. How much money is shown?

5. $0 \times 2 = ?$

6. Round *624* to the nearest hundred.

7. $728 - 354$

8. What time is it?

9. $5,324 \bigcirc 3,254$

10. Does this shape show a line of symmetry?

11. Which digit is in the hundreds place in *7,264*?

12. $333 + 468 = ?$

13. What fraction of the pie is shaded?

14. Put the numbers in order from least to greatest.

    365   1,254   987   125

15. How many children chose apples?

    How many more children chose
    grapes than peaches?

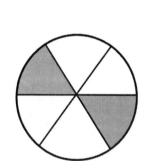

Favorite Fruits	
Fruit	**Votes**
Apples	~~HHH~~ ~~HHH~~
Bananas	////
Grapes	~~HHH~~ //
Peaches	///

1.	2.	3.
4.	5.	6.
7.	8.	9.
10.	11.	12.
13.	14.	15.

Lesson #122

1.   The number that occurs most often in a set is the _____.

2. $5 + 5 + 5 + 5 + 5 + 5 + 5$ is the same as 7×5. Both are equal to ____.

3.   Round *896* to the nearest hundred.

4. $69¢ + 23¢ = ?$

5.   Write the name of the shape.

6.   Count by twos.   92, 94, ____, 98, ____, ____

7.   Write the even numbers between *71* and *77*.

8.   What fraction of the pie is not shaded?

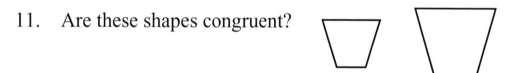

9. $757 - 139 = ?$

10.   Which digit is in the ones place in *6,531*?

11.   Are these shapes congruent?

12.   Count by fives.   75, ____, 85, ____, ____

13.   What is the time shown on the clock?

14.   How many minutes are in an hour?

15.   Lee read 28 pages on Monday. He read 16 pages on Tuesday and 23 more pages on Wednesday. How many pages did Lee read during the three days?

1.	2.	3.
4.	5.	6.
7.	8.	9.
10.	11.	12.
13.	14.	15.

Lesson #123

1. $4 \times 10 = ?$

2. What fraction of the rectangle is shaded?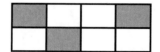

3. How much money is 5 quarters?

4. $3 + 8 = ?$

5. How much time has passed?

6. $406 + 538 = ?$

7. There are _____ minutes in a half-hour.

8. The sum is the answer to a(n) _____ problem.

9. Write the name of this shape.

10. $734 - 264 = ?$

11. $1,377 \bigcirc 946$

12. Round *526* to the nearest hundred.

13. $1 \times 5 = ?$

14. Write the first four odd numbers

15. How long is the arrow, in inches?

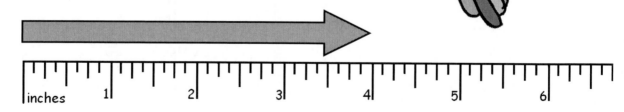

1.	2.	3.
4.	5.	6.
7.	8.	9.
10.	11.	12.
13.	14.	15.

Lesson #124

1. $408 + 564 = ?$

2. Leon used 3 feet of string on one kite, 2 feet for another kite, and 3 feet for a third kite. He had 12 feet of string left. How many feet of string did he begin with?

3. $743 \bigcirc 1,300$

4. Find the mode of 26, 34, 51, 26 and 30.

5. Round *305* to the nearest hundred.

6. $9 \times 2 = ?$

7. Which digit is in the thousands place in *6,427*?

8. $918 - 263 = ?$

9. $0 \times 5 = ?$

10. Does a feather weigh more than or less than a pound?

11. Arrange these numbers from greatest to least.   813, 650, 142, 436

12. Write the standard number for *three thousand, five hundred sixty-two.*

13. Is your desk 3 inches tall or 3 feet tall?

14. It is 12:00 now. What time will it be in 25 minutes?

15. How much money is shown?

1.	2.	3.
4.	5.	6.
7.	8.	9.
10.	11.	12.
13.	14.	15.

Lesson #125

1.   Draw two squares that are not congruent.

2.   The answer to a multiplication problem is the _____.

3. $345 + 549 = ?$

4.   Round *436* to the nearest hundred.

5.   How much money do you have if you have 6 quarters?

6. $5 + 5 + 5 + 5$ is the same as 4×5. Both are equal to _____.

7. $819 - 246 = ?$

8.   How much time has passed?

9. $0 \times 5 = ?$

10. Which digit is in the thousands place in *4,219*?

11. What fraction of the circle is shaded?

12. 2,375 ◯ 5,257

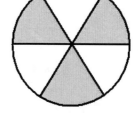

13. $2 + 4 + 9 = ?$

14. Count by tens.   240, 250, _____, _____, 280

15. How long is this piece
     of candy, in inches?

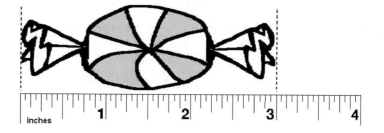

1.	2.	3.
4.	5.	6.
7.	8.	9.
10.	11.	12.
13.	14.	15.

Lesson #126

1. $9 + 7 = ?$

2. Are these cubes congruent?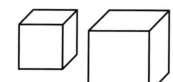

3. Round *58* to the nearest ten.

4. $10 + 10 + 10 + 10$ is the same as 4×10. Both are equal to _____.

5. Write the time shown on the clock.

6. $630 - 118 = ?$

7. List the even numbers between *21* and *25*.

8. Write the standard number for *six thousand, three hundred twenty-nine*.

9. What is the name of the shape?

10. How many inches are in a foot?

11. Which shaded fraction is greater?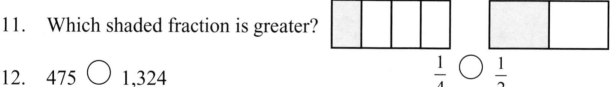

12. $475 \bigcirc 1,324$

$\dfrac{1}{4} \bigcirc \dfrac{1}{2}$

13. If it is12:00 now, what time will it be in 15 minutes?

14. Does a lamp weigh more than a pound or less than a pound?

15. Jason planted 25 seeds in one carton and 18 seeds in another carton. How many seeds did Jason plant in all?

1.	2.	3.
4.	5.	6.
7.	8.	9.
10.	11.	12.
13.	14.	15.

Lesson #127

1. Is *3,466* an even number or an odd number?

2. How much money is shown?

3. 314 + 486 = ?

4. Put the numbers in order from least to greatest.   27, 10, 39, 19, 41

5. Does this picture show a line of symmetry?

6. 2 + 2 + 2 + 2 + 2 is the same as 5 × 2. Both are equal to _____.

7. Which digit is in the tens place in *9,347*?

8. Draw a square and shade $\frac{1}{4}$ of it.

9. How many minutes are in a half-hour?

10. Is this figure a cube?

11. 852 – 327 = ?

12. The _____ is the answer to a subtraction problem.

13. Tommy has 5 trees in his yard. There are 2 birds in each tree. How many birds are in Tommy's yard?

14. Round *883* to the nearest hundred.

15. March 1st will be on what day of the week?

    What is the date 3 weeks after February 3rd?

February

S	M	T	W	T	F	S
						1
2	3	4	5	6	7	8
9	10	11	12	13	14	15
16	17	18	19	20	21	22
23	24	25	26	27	28	

1.	2.	3.
4.	5.	6.
7.	8.	9.
10.	11.	12.
13.	14.	15.

Lesson #128

1.   Write *534* using words.

2.   There are _____ quarts in a gallon.

3.   68¢ + 27¢ = ?

4.   Fill in the missing numbers.   365, ____, 385, ____

5.   How much time has passed?

6.   4 × 10 = ?

7.   967 − 481 = ?

8.   What fraction is not shaded?

9.   The sum is the answer to a(n) _____ problem.

10.   In the set of numbers, 18, 37, 26, 37 and 50, what is the mode?

11.   447 + 295 = ?

12.   How much money is shown here?

13.   Which is longer, 9 inches or 1 foot?

14.   12 ÷ 2 = ?

15.   What is the length of the piece of chalk in inches?

1.	2.	3.
4.	5.	6.
7.	8.	9.
10.	11.	12.
13.	14.	15.

Lesson #129

1. Which month comes before February?

2. 7,312 6,231

3. $5 + 5 + 5 + 5 + 5$ is the same as 5×5. Both are equal to _____.

4. There were 165 marbles in the jar. Jason gave 88 of those marbles to his friend, Ryan. How many marbles are left in the jar?

5. $721 + 239 = ?$

6. What is the name of the shape?

7. Round *573* to the nearest hundred.

8. $3 \times 2 = ?$

9. Draw a rectangle and show a line of symmetry on it.

10. Does a CD weigh more than or less than a pound?

11. It is 3:15 now. Draw a clock showing this time.

12. $560 - 247 = ?$

13. I have seven thousands, five hundreds, four tens and six ones. What number am I?

14. How many quarts are in a gallon?

15. How long does *Arts & Crafts* last?

    If you went to all of the park's activities, how long would you be at the park?

Park Schedule	
Time	Activity
1:30 – 2:00	Story Time
2:00 – 3:30	Arts & Crafts
3:30 – 4:30	Baseball

1.	2.	3.
4.	5.	6.
7.	8.	9.
10.	11.	12.
13.	14.	15.

Lesson #130

1. $64 + 29 = ?$

2. How much money is 10 quarters?

3. Draw 2 congruent triangles.

4. Which is longer, 30 minutes or 1 hour?

5. $635 - 326 = ?$

6. Put the numbers in order from greatest to least.

   3,156   6,516   1,653

7. $7 \times 2 = ?$

8. What fraction of the pie is shaded?

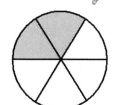

9. How many quarts are in a gallon?

10. What number comes between *257* and *430*?   145   567   358

11. Which digit is in the hundreds place in *2,964*?

12. Write the name of the shape.

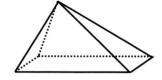

13. Is *227* closer to 200 or to 300?

14. It is 5:00. What time will it be in 10 minutes?

15. Kelly bought a pen for $2.45 and a sticker book for $1.75. How much money did she spend?

1.	2.	3.
4.	5.	6.
7.	8.	9.
10.	11.	12.
13.	14.	15.

Lesson #131

1. Which digit is in the thousands place in *7,056*?

2. Round *314* to the nearest hundred.

3. 466 + 427 = ?

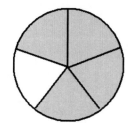

4. What fraction of the pie is shaded?

5. 2 + 2 + 2 + 2 + 2 + 2 is the same as 6 × 2. Both are equal to _____.

6. There are _____ inches in a foot.

7. Write the name of the figure.

8. 886 ◯ 952

9. Are the shapes congruent?

10. 73¢ − 25¢ = ?

11. Write the standard number for *three thousand, six hundred ninety-two*.

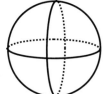
Start   End

12. How much time has passed?

13. 590 − 257 = ?

14. Which shaded part is larger?

$\frac{1}{6}$ ◯ $\frac{1}{4}$

15. Patrick spent $5.00 on popcorn. Which 2 bags did he buy?

    a) $3.50   b) $2.50   c) $1.50

1.	2.	3.
4.	5.	6.
7.	8.	9.
10.	11.	12.
13.	14.	15.

Lesson #132

1. $6.55 – $3.29 = ?

2.   Draw a rectangle and shade $\frac{3}{5}$ of it.

3.   Which digit is in the ones place in *937*?

4.   Order these numbers from least to greatest.   865   1,219   713   2,300

5.   3,257 + 1,651 = ?

6.   Does this figure show a line of symmetry?

7.   If Juan buys a ball for 60¢ and pays for it with 3 quarters, how much change will he get back?

8.   Which unit is used for measuring the length of your math book?

   a) inches   b) pounds   c) quarts

9.   Two shapes that are the same size and shape are _____.

10. Chris has 4 fish bowls in his room. There are 5 fish in each bowl. How many fish does Chris have? Make a picture to help you.

11. **This shape is a rectangular prism.** **It looks like a brick.** Write *rectangular prism* in the box.

12. Round *934* to the nearest hundred.

13. 3 × 2 = ?

14. How much money is 5 quarters?

15. Which thermometer shows a good temperature for swimming?

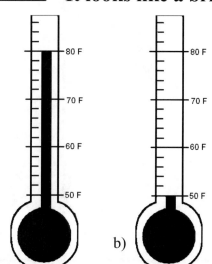

1.	2.	3.
4.	5.	6.
7.	8.	9.
10.	11.	12.
13.	14.	15.

Lesson #133

1. $5 + 8 = ?$

2. How much money is shown here?

3. Round *764* to the nearest hundred.

4. The number that is seen most often in a set is the _____.

5. $835 - 392 = ?$

6. Write the even numbers between *31* and *37*.

7. I have 6 hundreds, 9 tens and 3 ones. What number am I?

8. What is the name of this shape?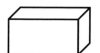

9. $2,446 + 4,378 = ?$

10. $3 \times 5 = ?$

11. Which digit is in the hundreds place in *3,815*?

12. How many days are in a year?

13. $8 \div 2 = ?$

14. 4,352 ◯ 4,624

15. How long, in inches, is the rectangle?

1.

2.

3.

4.

5.

6.

7.

8.

9.

10.

11.

12.

13.

14.

15.

Lesson #134

1. $2 \times 5 = ?$

2. Round *216* to the nearest hundred.

3. $62 - 47 = ?$

4. There were 37 birds in a tree. As a cat walked
    toward the tree, 18 of the birds flew away.
    How many birds are still in the tree?

5. Is *8,649* an even or an odd number?

6. $2,366 + 1,475 = ?$

7. Are these shapes congruent?

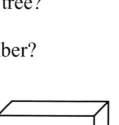

8. $0 \times 10 = ?$

9. What fraction of the pie is not shaded?

10. Which digit is in the thousands place in *7,306*?

11. Count by fives.   85, ____, ____, 100, ____

12. Does a baby weigh more than a pound or less than a pound?

13. What time is shown on the clock?

14. Which is greater, 7 dimes or $1.00?

15. Kendra picked some apples and has put them in bags. She has 3
    bags, with 5 apples in each bag. How many apples did Kendra
    pick?

1.	2.	3.
4.	5.	6.
7.	8.	9.
10.	11.	12.
13.	14.	15.

Lesson #135

1. 3,508 + 3,196 = ?

2. Does a piano weigh more than or less than a pound?

3. Draw two congruent rectangles.

4. Round *388* to the nearest hundred.

5. Write the name of the shape.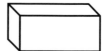

6. 703 – 481 = ?

7. The difference is the answer to a(n) _____ problem.

8. 10 ÷ 2 = ?

9. 6 + 9 = ?

10. How much time has passed?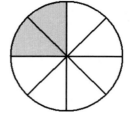

11. 0 × 5 = ?

12. *86* is the _____ of these numbers.   37, 29, 86, 53, 86

13. 8,342 ◯ 6,856

14. What fraction of the pie is shaded?

15. What is the length of the arrow in inches?

1.	2.	3.
4.	5.	6.
7.	8.	9.
10.	11.	12.
13.	14.	15.

Lesson #136

1. Write *653* using words.

2. What is the name of this shape?

3. Which digit is in the tens place in *9,132*?

4. Write a fact family for 5, 6 and 11.

5. How much money is shown?

6. 935 – 682 = ?

7. Would you measure the weight of your dog in feet, pounds or in quarts?

8. How many minutes are in a half-hour?

9. 518 + 279 = ?

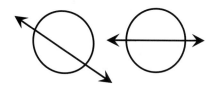

10. Draw the shape that shows two equal parts.

11. Write the odd numbers between *30* and *36*.

12. What time is shown on the clock?

13. 5 × 5 = ?

14. Does it take 20 minutes or 20 hours to cut the grass?

15. How many total insects were in the yard?

    How many more ants than grasshoppers were there?

Insects in the Yard

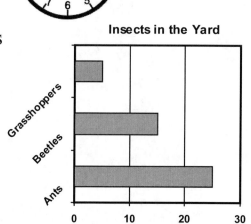

1.	2.	3.
4.	5.	6.
7.	8.	9.
10.	11.	12.
13.	14.	15.

Lesson #137

1. I have six thousands, three hundreds, two tens and five ones. What number am I?

2. Write the name of the shape.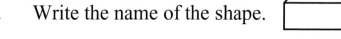

3. $35 + 21 + 13 = ?$

4. Are these shapes congruent?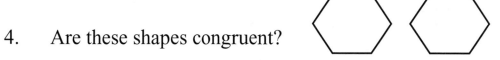

5. The answer to a multiplication problem is the _____.

6. How much time has passed?

7. $630 - 428 = ?$

8. Is the number *4,315* even or odd?

9. Eight quarters are the same amount of money as two _____.

10. $9 \times 2 = ?$

11. Order these numbers from greatest to least.

    455   1,231   786   239

12. Round *56* to the nearest ten.

13. $3,452 \bigcirc 3,524$

14. Write *734* using words.

15. How many days are in July?
    On which day of the week is July 24th?

July

S	M	T	W	T	F	S
					1	2
3	4	5	6	7	8	9
10	11	12	13	14	15	16
17	18	19	20	21	22	23
24	25	26	27	28	29	30
31						

1.	2.	3.
4.	5.	6.
7.	8.	9.
10.	11.	12.
13.	14.	15.

Lesson #138

1. There are _____ quarts in a gallon.

2. $864 + 99 = ?$

3. What is the name of this shape?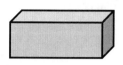

4. Which digit is in the hundreds place in *6,498*?

5. What number comes just before *1,000*?

6. What temperature is shown on the thermometer?

7. Draw 2 squares that are not congruent.

8. Write the time shown on the clock.

9. $724 - 516 = ?$

10. Marcus bought a football for $3.75. He gave the clerk $5.00. How much change did he receive?

11. Write *985* using words.

12. How much money is shown here?

13. $5 + 5 + 5 + 5 + 5 + 5$ is the same as 6×5. Both are equal to _____.

14. Order the numbers from least to greatest.

    3,475   2,199   3,056   2,516

15. What fraction of the rectangle is not shaded?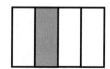

1.	2.	3.
4.	5.	6.
7.	8.	9.
10.	11.	12.
13.	14.	15.

Lesson #139

1. Round *767* to the nearest hundred.

2. $843 - 375 = ?$

3. Write the name of this shape.

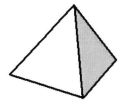

4. Draw 2 congruent triangles.

5. A number has 3 thousands, 6 hundreds, 5 tens and 4 ones. What is the number?

6. 2,416 ◯ 2,146

7. Which would you use to measure the temperature?

    a) scale   b) ruler   c) thermometer

8. How many hours are in a day?

9. $538 + 277 = ?$

10. How much money is shown?

11. $6 \times 2 = ?$

12. Is the number *8,314* even or odd?

13. Does this picture show a line of symmetry?

14. Which is longer, 3 weeks or 1 month?

15. How long is the pencil, in inches?

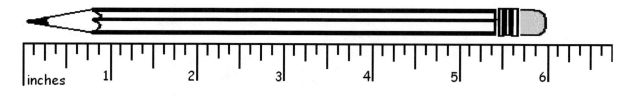

1.	2.	3.
4.	5.	6.
7.	8.	9.
10.	11.	12.
13.	14.	15.

Lesson #140

1. Which digit is in the ones place in *4,386*?

2. 8,585 + 397 = ?

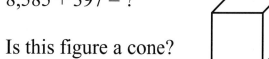

3. Is this figure a cone?

4. Count by tens.   340, 350, ___, ____, _____

5. Round *416* to the nearest hundred.

6. What time is it?

7. $2.85 − $1.79 = ?

8. 2,314 ◯ 2,143

9. Does it take 7 seconds or 7 minutes to get dressed?

10. What fraction of this rhombus is shaded?

11. 4 × 5 = ?

12. The number that occurs most often in a set is the _____.

13. Twenty nickels are the same amount of money as one _____.

14. Are these shapes congruent?

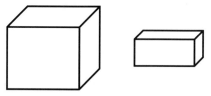

15. There are 47 students in the school band. Twenty-three students play a wind instrument. How many students <u>do not</u> play a wind instrument?

1.	2.	3.
4.	5.	6.
7.	8.	9.
10.	11.	12.
13.	14.	15.

Level 2

Help Pages

Help Pages

Vocabulary

Arithmetic Operations
Addition → When you combine numbers, you add. The sign "+" means add. The answer to an addition problem is called the *sum*. Example: When you combine 5 and 2, the sum is 7; $5 + 2 = 7$.
Subtraction → When you take one number away from another, you subtract. The sign "−" means subtract. The answer to a subtraction problem is called the *difference*. Example: When you take 1 away from 5, the difference is 4; $5 - 1 = 4$.
Multiplication → When you add a number to itself so many times, you multiply. The sign "x" means multiply. The answer to a multiplication problem is called the *product*. Example: When 5 is added to itself 3 times, the product is 15; $5 + 5 + 5$ is the same as $3 \times 5 = 15$.
Division → When you share equally, you divide. The sign "÷" means divide. The answer to a division problem is called the *quotient*. Example: When 8 is shared equally between 2, the quotient is 4; $8 ÷ 2 = 4$.

Geometry
Congruent — figures with the same shape and the same size.
Fraction — a part of a whole. Example: ⊞ This box has 4 parts. 1 part is shaded. $\frac{1}{4}$
Line of Symmetry — a line along which a figure can be folded so that the two halves match exactly.

Geometry — Shapes and Solids

Cone —	△	Pyramid —	◁
Cube —	⬛	Rectangular Prism —	▭
Cylinder —	⬭	Rhombus (diamond) —	◇
Ellipse (oval) —	⬭	Sphere —	⊕

Help Pages

Vocabulary

Geometry — Polygons			
Number of Sides	**Name**	**Number of Sides**	**Name**
3 △	Triangle	4 ☐	Quadrilateral

Measurement — Relationships	
Time	**Distance**
30 minutes = 1 half-hour	12 inches = 1 foot
60 minutes = 1 hour	**Volume**
365 days = 1 year	4 quarts = 1 gallon

Statistics

Mode — the number that occurs most often in a group of numbers. The mode is found by counting how many times each number occurs in the list. The number that occurs more than any other is the mode. Some groups of numbers have more than one mode.

Example: The mode of 77, (93), 85, (93), 77, 81, (93), and 71 is **93**.
(93 is the mode because it occurs more than the others.)

Place Value

Whole Numbers
1, 4 0 5
Thousands Hundreds Tens Ones

The number above is read: one thousand, four hundred five.

Help Pages

Solved Examples

Whole Numbers (continued)

When we **round numbers**, we are estimating them. This means we focus on a particular place value, and decide if that digit is closer to the next higher number (round up) or to the next lower number (keep the same). It might be helpful to look at the place-value chart on page 141.

Example: Round 347 to the tens place.

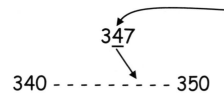

347 is closer to 350, so it is rounded to 350.

350

1. Identify the place that you want to round to.
2. What are the nearest "tens" on either side of the number? (340 and 350)
3. Which of these is 347 closer to?
4. This is the number you round to.

Here is another example of rounding whole numbers.

Examples: Round 83 to the nearest ten.

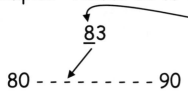

83 is closer to 80, so it is rounded to 80.

80

1. What is the rounding place?
2. What are the nearest "tens" on either side of the number? (80 and 90)
3. Which of these is 83 closer to?
4. This is the number you round to.

Help Pages

Solved Examples

Whole Numbers (continued)

There are **even numbers** and **odd numbers**. A number is <u>even</u> if it ends in 0, 2, 4, 6 or 8. A number is <u>odd</u> if it ends in 1, 3, 5, 7 or 9.

Examples: 46 is an even number because it ends in 6.

11 is an odd number because it ends in 1.

A **fact family** is a set of related facts using addition, subtraction, and the same three numbers.

Example: Write a fact family using 3, 4 and 7.

$$3 + 4 = 7 \qquad 7 - 3 = 4$$
$$4 + 3 = 7 \qquad 7 - 4 = 3$$

Numbers can be compared by saying one is **greater than** another or one is **less than** another.

The symbol ">" means *greater than*. The symbol "<" means *less than*.

Hint: The open part of the sign is near the bigger number.

Examples: 10 is less than 18. → 10 $<$ 18

27 is greater than 13. → 27 $>$ 13

Help Pages

Solved Examples

Whole Numbers (continued)

When adding or subtracting whole numbers, first the numbers must be lined-up from the right. Starting with the ones place, add (or subtract) the numbers. When adding, if the answer has 2 digits, write the ones digit and regroup the tens digit. For subtraction, it may also be necessary to regroup first. Then, add (or subtract) the numbers in the tens place. Continue with the hundreds, etc.

Look at these examples of **addition**.

Examples: Find the sum of 314 and 12.   Add 648 and 236.

```
  314
+  12
-----
  326
```

1. Line up the numbers on the right.
2. Beginning with the ones place, add. Regroup if necessary.
3. Repeat with the tens place.
4. Continue this process with the hundreds place, etc.

```
   1
  648
+ 236
-----
  884
```

Use the following examples of **subtraction** to help you.

Example: Subtract 37 from 93.

```
  8  13
  9  3
-  3  7
-------
  5  6
```

1. Begin with the ones place. Check to see if you need to regroup. Since 7 is larger than 3, you must regroup to 8 tens and 13 ones.
2. Now look at the tens place. Check to see if you need to regroup. Since 3 is less than 8, you do not need to regroup.
3. Subtract each place value beginning with the ones.

Help Pages

Solved Examples

Whole Numbers (continued)

Example: Find the difference of 425 and 233.

$$\begin{array}{r} {}^{3}\cancel{4}\,{}^{12}\cancel{2}5 \\ -\ 2\,3\,3 \\ \hline 1\,9\,2 \end{array}$$

1. Begin with the ones place. Check to see if you need to regroup. Since 3 is less than 5, you do not need to regroup.
2. Now look at the tens place. Check to see if you need to regroup. Since 3 is larger than 2, you must regroup to 3 hundreds and 12 tens.
3. Now look at the hundreds place. Check to see if you need to regroup. Since 2 is less than 3, you are ready to subtract.
4. Subtract each place value beginning with the ones.

Sometimes when doing subtraction, you must **subtract from zero**. You will always need to regroup. Use the examples below to help you.

Example: Subtract 38 from 60.

$$\begin{array}{r} {}^{5}\cancel{6}\,{}^{10}\cancel{0} \\ -\ 3\,8 \\ \hline 2\,2 \end{array}$$

1. Begin with the ones place. Since 8 is less than 0, you must regroup.
2. Regroup to 5 tens and 10 ones.
3. Then, subtract each place value beginning with the ones.

Example: Find the difference between 500 and 261.

$$\begin{array}{r} {}^{4}\cancel{5}\,{}^{9}{}^{10}\cancel{0}\,{}^{10}\cancel{0} \\ -\ 2\,6\,1 \\ \hline 2\,3\,9 \end{array}$$

Help Pages

Solved Examples

Whole Numbers (continued)

Multiplication is a quicker way to add groups of numbers. The sign (×) for multiplication is read "times." The answer to a multiplication problem is called the product. Use the examples below to help you understand multiplication.

Example: 2 × 5 is read "two times five."

It means *2 groups of 5* or 5 + 5.

2 × 5 = 5 + 5 = **10**

The product of 2 × 5 is **10**.

Example: 5 × 4 is read "five times four."

It means *5 groups of 4* or 4 + 4 + 4 + 4 + 4.

5 × 4 = 4 + 4 + 4 + 4 + 4 = **20**

The product of 5 × 4 is **20**.

It is very important that you memorize your **multiplication facts**. This table will help you, but only until you memorize them!

To use this table, choose a number in the top gray box and multiply it by a number in the left gray box. Follow both with your fingers (down and across) until they meet. The number in that box is the product.

An example is shown for you:

2 × 5 = 10

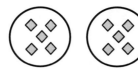

×	0	1	2	5	10
0	0	0	0	0	0
1	0	1	2	5	10
2	0	2	4	10	20
5	0	5	10	25	50
10	0	10	20	50	100

Help Pages

Solved Examples

Whole Numbers (continued)

Division is the opposite of multiplication. The sign (÷) for division is read "divided by." The answer to a division problem is called the quotient.

Remember that multiplication is a way of adding groups to get their total. Think of division as the opposite of this. In division, you already know the total and the number in each group. You want to know how many groups there are. Follow the examples below.

Example: What is 9 ÷ 3?   (9 items divided into groups of 3)

The total number is 9.

Each group contains 3.

How many groups are there?   There are 3 groups.

$$9 \div 3 = \mathbf{3}$$

Divide 10 by 2.   (10 items divided into groups of 2)

The total number is 10.

Each group contains 2.

How many groups are there?   There are 5 groups.

$$10 \div 2 = \mathbf{5}$$

Fractions

A **fraction** is used to represent part of a whole. The top number in a fraction is the part. The bottom number in a fraction is the whole.

The whole rectangle has 6 sections.

Only 1 section is shaded.

This can be shown as the fraction $\frac{1}{6}$.

$$\frac{1}{6} \quad \frac{\text{shaded part}}{\text{parts in the whole}}$$

Help Pages

Solved Examples

Time

The measure of how long something takes to happen is called **elapsed time**.

Example:

The movie began at 7:00 and ended at 9:00. How long did the movie last? (How much time passed between 7:00 and 9:00?)   There are **2 hours** between 7:00 and 9:00.

Example:

How many hours pass from the beginning of Spelling class until the end of Math class?

Spelling starts at 8:30. Math ends at 11:30. (How much time passes between 8:30 and 11:30?)

There are **3 hours** between 8:30 and 11:30.

Class Schedule

8:30 – 9:00	Spelling
9:00 – 10:00	Reading
10:00 – 11:30	Math
11:30 – 12:00	English

Help Pages

"Who Knows?"

Sides in a triangle?...(3)

Sides in a square?..(4)

Days in a week? ....(7)

Months in a year? ....(12)

Days in a year? ....(365)

Inches in a foot?...(12)

Quarts in a gallon?..(4)

The number that is seen most
often in a set of numbers?.......................... (mode)

Figures with the same size
and shape? ....(congruent)

Answer to an addition problem?.....................(sum)

Answer to a subtraction problem? ....(difference)

Answer to a multiplication
problem?..(product)